DOLPHINS
on the
SAND

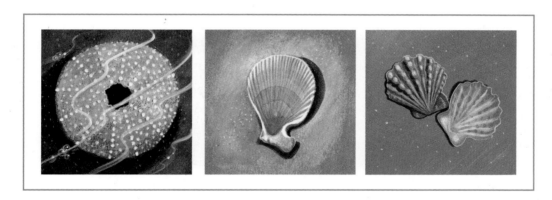

~ JIM ARNOSKY ~

SCHOLASTIC INC.
New York Toronto London Auckland
Sydney Mexico City New Delhi Hong Kong

ISBN 978-0-545-45927-3

12 11 10 9 8 7 6 5 4 3 2 1   12 13 14 15 16 17/0

Printed in the U.S.A.   08

First Scholastic printing, January 2012

Design by Richard Amari
Text set in Kennerly
The artist used acrylic applied in thick opaque layers on
paper to create the illustrations for this book.

For Susannah

They came in over the reef from deep water. A dozen dolphins swimming fast. Dolphins racing and leaping, chasing a school of fish. Leading the chase was the oldest dolphin with her swift and agile youngster.

The dolphins swam against an outgoing tide as they pursued the fish closer and closer to the shore. Suddenly, the lead dolphin began slowing down. Tired from the chase, she turned away from the fleeing fish and swam to the shallow water near a long sandbar. There she beached herself and rested. The young dolphin and all the other dolphins followed, skidding and sliding to a stop on the sand.

The tide kept rushing out. The water near the sandbar quickly became dangerously low. The mother dolphin felt a strong urge to lead her baby back to deeper water. She squirmed around and faced the sea. But there was not enough water to swim.

All of the dolphins wriggled around on the sand, struggling to swim. But, with deeper water now so far away, they could not escape. They were stranded on the sandbar.

By the time the tide began creeping back in, the dolphins had been lying on the sand for hours. All were exhausted and dehydrated from being out of the water.

Feeling sick and dizzy, the young dolphin lay against his mother. He nudged her with his head until she made some low sounds. The sun was sinking below the horizon.

A kayaker gliding by spotted the beached dolphins and paddled to shore to get help.

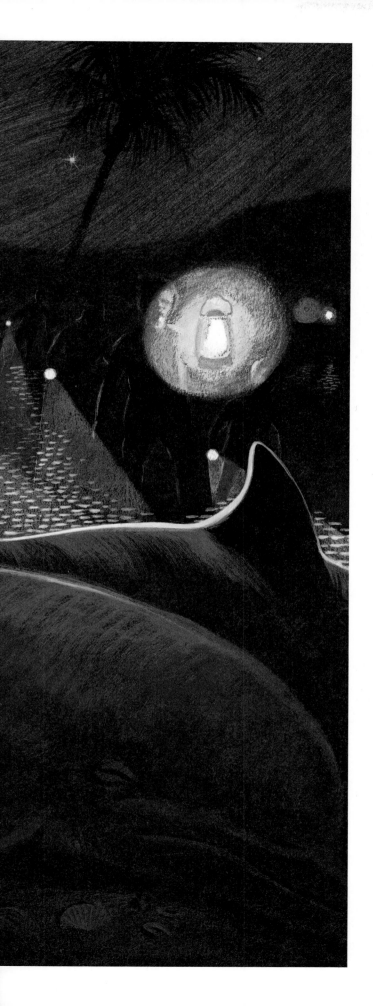

After dark, the first rescue
boat came, shining a spotlight
on the stranded dolphins.
A little while later, more
rescuers came in boats and
on foot, carrying flashlights
and lanterns.

At first, the young dolphin was frightened by the bright light and shadowy shapes. Then one rescuer knelt beside him and gently wiped the sand away from his mouth and eyes. The little dolphin felt cool water being splashed on his back and sides.

The rescuers comforted all the dolphins into the night.

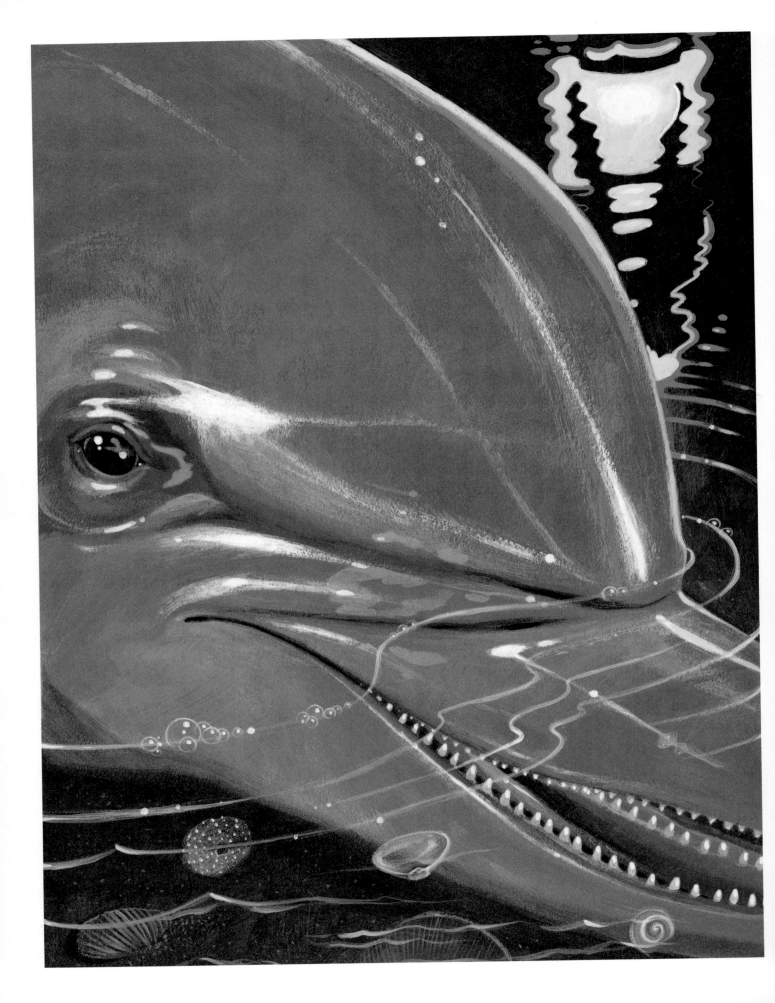

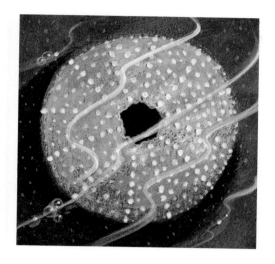

When the tide began flowing back in over the
sandbar, the young dolphin felt strong enough to
try and swim. But the water was still too shallow.
As the tidewater washed around him, he called
to his mother in clicking and squeaking sounds,
until he heard her weakly calling back.

Out in deeper water, the dark fins of hungry sharks sliced through blue-black waves. The sharks cruised back and forth, waiting to ambush the weakened dolphins once they tried to swim.

The tide kept pushing in, and the sharks swam closer. Some of the rescuers shined their lights on the prowling sharks, while others moved the dolphins to a safe lagoon near shore.

In the safety of a shoreline lagoon brightly lit
by the rescuers' lights, the dolphins swam for the
first time since their stranding. The old mother,
though, was still too weak to swim. She closed her
eyes and rolled on her side in the water. The young
dolphin squeaked softly to her until she recovered
enough to swim slowly but steadily in the lagoon.

The tide came and went in the night, and
came back again at first light. Morning dawned,
brightening the water with the hazy colors of a
new day. The dolphins swam round and round
in the lagoon, getting stronger with every turn.

Then one by one the dolphins were allowed to leave the lagoon and swim back out to sea, but only after each was corralled and observed to see if it was strong enough.

When the rescuers tried to corral him and his mother, the young dolphin escaped by swimming under a tangle of mangrove trees. And there he stayed while his mother was being caught and held in the water.

When his mother was finally let go, the little dolphin dashed out to join her. Together again, they swam in happy circles, chattering to each other in high-pitched clicks.

With the tide high and deep, they swam past the rescue boats, out of the shoreline lagoon, over the submerged sandbar and back to the freedom of the sea.

AUTHOR'S NOTE

Nobody knows for sure why dolphins and whales occasionally become stranded on the sand. The theories range from the animals simply beaching themselves in order to rest to them being disoriented by the sonar soundings of big ships. Whatever the reasons they become stranded, being out of the water a long while can be fatal: they suffer from dehydration and from the impact on their internal organs from their own heavy weight when normally they are buoyant in the water.

Not long ago Deanna and I witnessed a stranding of dolphins and the subsequent rescue efforts of people of all ages, from all walks of life, to comfort and help the animals. This book is an idealized account of what we saw.

Jim Arnosky

Einstein Elementary School
18025 NE 116 St
Redmond, Wash. 98052

DOLPHINS are swift, graceful masters of the ocean. But when a pod of dolphins gets stranded on a sandbar, it is up to a few dedicated people to save them, bringing the dolphins to the safety of a lagoon and protecting them until they are strong enough to swim back out to sea.

Jim Arnosky presents an intimate look at a dolphin rescue, revealing the challenges and the drama of saving dolphins on the sand.

Cover art © 2008 by Jim Arnosky

SCHOLASTIC

www.scholastic.com

ISBN 978-0-545-45927-3

$4.99 US

50499

9 780545 459273

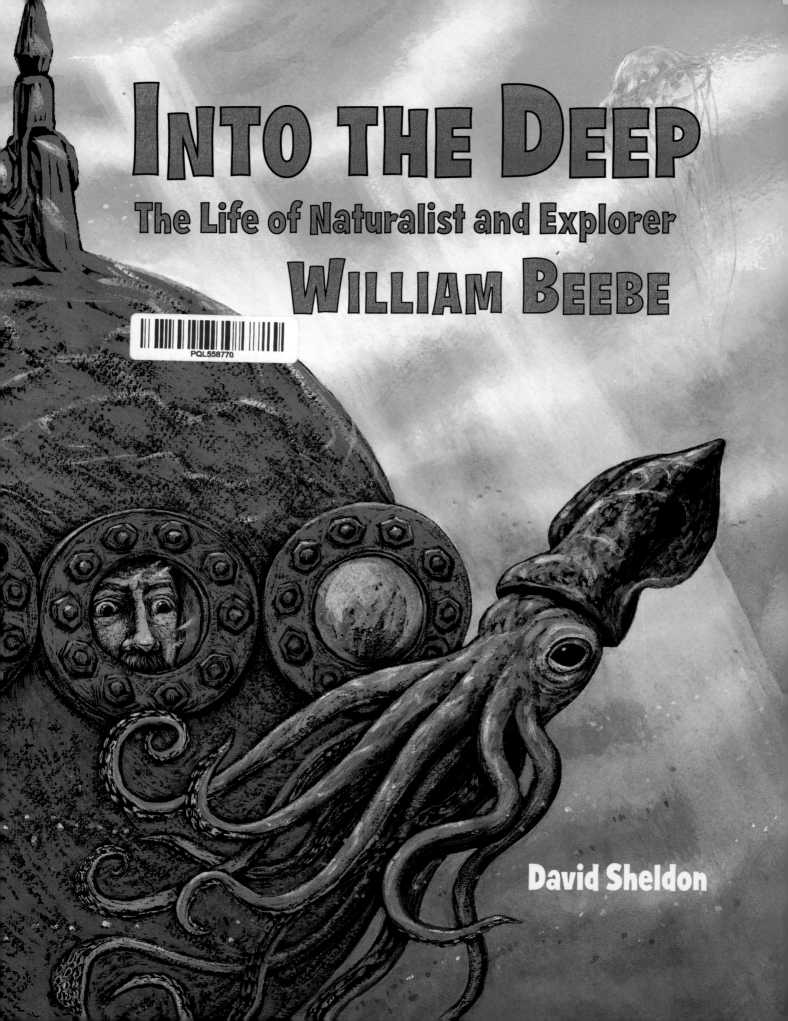

INTO THE DEEP
The Life of Naturalist and Explorer
WILLIAM BEEBE

David Sheldon